Little G and Big C

by Connie Massingill

RoseDog Books
PITTSBURGH, PENNSYLVANIA 15238

The contents of this work including, but not limited to, the accuracy of events, people, and places depicted; opinions expressed; permission to use previously published materials included; and any advice given or actions advocated are solely the responsibility of the author, who assumes all liability for said work and indemnifies the publisher against any claims stemming from publication of the work.

RoseDog Books
585 Alpha Drive
Suite 103
Pittsburgh, PA 15238
Visit our website at *www.rosedogbookstore.com*

ISBN: 978-1-64957-945-4
eISBN: 978-1-64957-966-9

EPHESIANS 4:32

And be ye kind to one another, tenderhearted, forgiving one another, even as God for Christ's sake hath forgiven you.

I dedicate this book to my sister, Gina Childs Griffis

Little G
and Big C

Little G was a kind soul.

Little G always wore a huge smile.

Little G believed in sharing her love.

Little G always helped others.

Little G always fed others.

Little G always gave to others.

One day, little G gave her sister,
big C, a beautiful pink flower.

Big C loved the beautiful
pink flower in the green pot.

As the days and weeks went by,
big C forgot about
the beautiful pink flower.

Big C did not water the pink flower.
She did not give
the pink flower sunshine.
She did not give
the pink flower any attention.

The beautiful pink flower
was no longer pink, nor beautiful.
The flower had lost its bloom
and lost its beautiful green leaves.

One day, big C saw little G
working in her garden.
Little G had her huge smile on her face.
Her smile made big C smile.

Seeing little G's big smile made big C
remember her not so beautiful pink flower.

Big C went home and apologized
to the not so beautiful flower.

Big C started giving
the flower lots of attention.
She sang to her flower,
she watered her flower.
She made sure the flower
got lots of sunshine and love.

After several weeks of love and care,
the flower began to grow.
It now had beautiful, healthy green leaves
and a big beautiful pink bloom.

Big C now wears
a huge smile on her face
just like her sister little G.

CPSIA information can be obtained
at www.ICGtesting.com
Printed in the USA
BVHW020804071221
623348BV00019B/198

* 9 7 8 1 6 4 9 5 7 9 4 5 4 *